Contents

Look at them go!
Focus on: j as in *jet* 3

Let's look
Focus on: all as in *b<u>all</u>* 8

Red Robot runs
Focus on: r as in *<u>r</u>un* 13

Look, quick!
Focus on: qu as in *<u>qu</u>iz* 18

Scan to listen along!

Audio to accompany this book can be streamed online with a mobile or tablet using this QR code:

About this book

These short stories are designed to give young children blending and reading practice. They are decodable, which means the words in them only include letter shapes and sounds that the children have learned. The stories also gradually introduce a few 'tricky' words, which are essential for children to become familiar with, such as 'they', 'of' and 'said'.

As children progress through these readers, new letter sounds and 'tricky' words are added and previous learning is revised. The progression links directly to the teaching order and lessons in the Letterland *Teacher's Guides* (UK and US versions). Each story begins with a title page that provides important information for children and teachers.

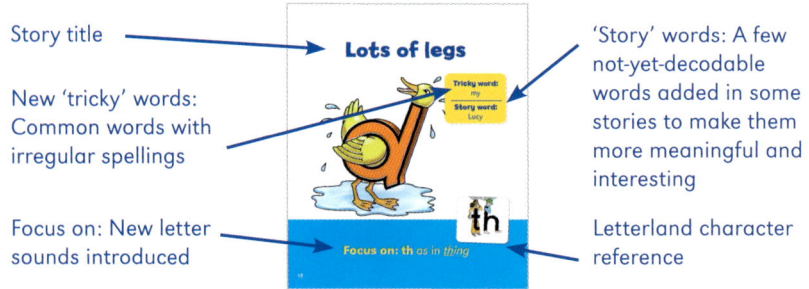

Story title

New 'tricky' words: Common words with irregular spellings

Focus on: New letter sounds introduced

'Story' words: A few not-yet-decodable words added in some stories to make them more meaningful and interesting

Letterland character reference

Basic teaching tips:

- Encourage the sounding out of decodable words (and any decodable parts of 'tricky' words).
- Discuss the stories with the children to ensure comprehension and engagement.
- Encourage re-reading in pairs or individually to develop fluency and reading for meaning.

See **www.letterland.com/Phonics-Readers** and the latest editions of the Letterland **Teacher's Guides** for more suggestions on how to use this book.

Look at them go!

Focus on: j as in *jet*

Look at Jim go!

That jet can go, go, go!

Can she jog?
Yes, she can!

We go on the bus.
Look at us go!

Let's look

Focus on: all as in *ball*

Hat Man sees all the hats. But he cannot see his hat! Can you?

Ben looks for his ball. Can you see his ball?

Can you see the dog in the fog?

The cat is looking for her cup.
"Can you help me?" she calls.

Red Robot runs

Tricky word: robot

Focus on: r as in *run*

Red Robot gets a red rug.
He runs off.

He gets a big ring.

Off he runs.

Red Robot sees a rat.

Red Robot just runs!
No rat, no rug, no ring.

Look, quick!

Tricky word: was

Story words: Queen, Munching Mike

Focus on: qu as in *quiz*